GRO... THE AWFUL TRUTH

Scoular Anderson

Hodder
Children's
Books

a division of Hodder Headline Limited

For the staff and pupils of
Innellan Primary School
who

SPLOT!

helped with this book.

Text and illustrations copyright 1999 © Scoular Anderson
Published by Hodder Children's Books 1999

Book design by Joy Mutter
Cover illustration by Scoular Anderson

The right of Scoular Anderson to be identified as the author and
illustrator of the work has been asserted by him in accordance with
the Copyright, Designs and Patents Act 1988.

10 9 8 7 6 5 4 3

A catalogue record for this book is available from the British Library.

ISBN: 0 340 73616 X

Printed and bound by the Guernsey Press Co. Ltd,
Guernsey, Channel Islands.

Hodder Children's Books
a division of Hodder Headline Limited
338 Euston Road
London NW1 3BH

CONTENTS

GROWN-UPS
JUST WHAT ARE THEY LIKE?

This Book is about Grown-ups or Groanups as they are sometimes called. Here are some examples of Grown-ups:

Here are a few things you will notice about Grown-ups:

1 They are usually taller and wider than you.

2 They are usually lumpier and bumpier than you.

3 They are older than you. Most of them are ancient.

Some of them are almost nineteen. Others are about 500.

4 They are cleverer than you (or so they think).

Don't be so silly!

But now it's time to take a closer look at Grown-ups. To find out the AWFUL TRUTH about Grown-ups we will have to use a secret weapon – a pet animal . . .

. . . the Robotic Computer called CATAMOG. Catamog can watch Grown-ups closely without being seen.

The Catamog can tune in while flaked out on the sofa.

The Catamog can secretly hang in wardrobes and cupboards.

The Catamog can crouch in car engines . . .

. . . peer out from washing machines . . .

. . . hover in offices . . .

lurk under carpets.

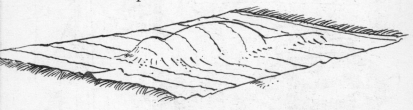

In fact, Catamog will go anywhere . . .

. . . to find out the AWFUL TRUTH about Grown-ups.

Catamog has been listening to Grown-ups being bossy. Grown-ups do this a lot.

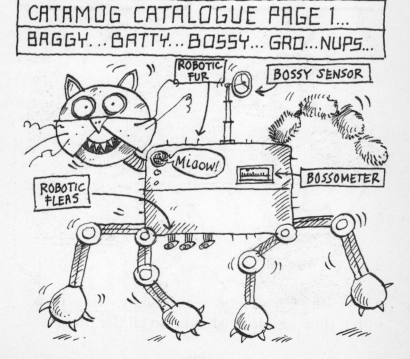

Catamog has discovered an AWFUL TRUTH.
Grown-ups think their childrens' brains are only
plastic models.

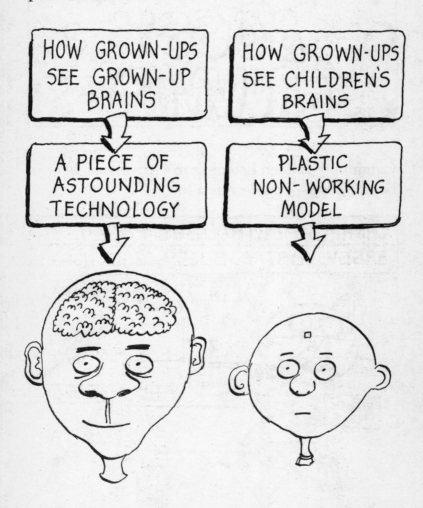

That's why Grown-ups are so bossy – they have
to tell their children what to do all the time.

The AWFUL TRUTH is that a lot of their bossiness gets very confusing.

Another AWFUL TRUTH about bossy
Grown-ups is that, no matter how old you are,
you will always be bossed around by a Grown-up.

THE AWFUL TRUTH ABOUT GROWN-UP SHOPPING

Catamog is taking his shopping basket to watch the Grown-ups in the shops.

ITEM SELECTOR

SHOPPING BASKET

MIAOW MUCH?

TROLLEY MODE

MONEY DISPENSER

SHOPPING LIST

Be on your guard
when a Grown-up
says the
dreaded words . . .

> I'm going to the supermarket. You can come and help.

At the supermarket you will probably be put in charge of the trolley, which is fine at first . . .

. . . but it will get a bit boring after a while because the Grown-up needs to concentrate very hard and you will have to keep silent.

Even if you try to be helpful by pointing something out on the shelf you will be told . . .

Shopping on a Sunday can be even worse. You will have to follow the Grown-up round a DIY store. The Grown-up will wander in a trance up and down the aisles.

The Grown-up will closely examine packets of sandpaper.

The Grown-up will do a calculation about plastic beading.

The Grown-up will compare the different pot-sizes of adhesive.

The Grown-up will measure bits of wood.

Two hours later, the Grown-up will head for the check-out with a packet of five screws.

Shopping for clothes takes even longer. Grown-ups can take about half a day to buy a t-shirt.

The worst kind of Grown-up shopping is when they are shopping for *you*. The AWFUL TRUTH is that the Grown-ups think they're shopping for someone else entirely.

The AWFUL TRUTH is that shopping with a Grown-up is bad for your health so when you hear the words . . .

. . . make a quick exit . . .

. . . and don't come out until the coast is clear.

THE AWFUL TRUTH ABOUT GROWN-UPS AND TIDINESS

Catamog has been studying Grown-ups and tidiness. There is tidiness and untidiness, there is tidy untidiness, there is messy neatness, and neat untidiness. Catamog is very confused.

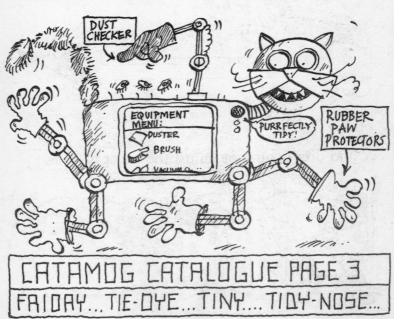

DUST CHECKER

EQUIPMENT MENU:
DUSTER
BRUSH
VACUUM CL...

PURRFECTLY TIDY!

RUBBER PAW PROTECTORS

CATAMOG CATALOGUE PAGE 3

FRIDAY... TIE-DYE... TINY.... TIDY-NOSE...

Alarm bells should sound in your head when a Grown-up says . . .

You should be even more worried when a Grown-up arrives at the door of your room with the Weapons of Tidiness.

Take a look at these two rooms . . .

BORING GROWN-UP ROOM

The AWFUL TRUTH is that every now and then, Grown-ups will want to attack your room with the Weapons of Tidiness. They think your room should be as boring as theirs.

They will listen to no excuses.

They will take
things away to be
cleaned.

They will tell you you're too old for some things
and they'll take them away from you.

They will tell you you've got too many things stuck on your wall.

They will tell you you've grown out of your Boys-R-Us socks and t-shirt.

They might even find your collection of dead spiders . . .

They will not stop until . . .

They feel they've tidied your room properly.

THE AWFUL TRUTH ABOUT GROWN-UPS AND FOOD

Catamog has disguised himself as a fish finger so he can find out the AWFUL TRUTH about food and Grown-ups.

CATAMOG CATALOGUE PAGE 4
FOAM...FOOTBALL...FOODBELL...FOOD...

The AWFUL TRUTH about Grown-ups is that they are just like the food they make. Grown-ups who get frothed, stirred and over-heated in the kitchen . . .

. . . will cook something frothed, stirred and over-heated to eat.

Grown-ups who are slow, thoughtful and painstaking in the kitchen . . .

. . . will dish up something weird and experimental.

Lots of Grown-ups are somewhere in between.

Many Grown-ups will try hard to please.

Grown-ups have a habit of stealing some of your food . . .

or maybe even all of it if you don't eat quickly enough.

On the other hand, if you eat too slowly Grown-ups will tell you . . .

But Grown-ups have no idea what this means. If you aren't doing this with your food . . .

. . . then you aren't really playing with it, are you?

One final note: Never complain about the food as this will bring on a furious Grown-up tantrum.

THE AWFUL TRUTH ABOUT GROWN-UPS AND SPORTS AND PASTIMES

Catamog has been watching how Grown-ups spend their spare time. They get up to some very strange things.

CATAMOG CATALOGUE PAGE 5
SPOTS... SPROUTS... SPORTS AND PASTIES...

SPORTS AND PAWSTIMES!

SPORTY WHEELS

ENCYCLOPAEDIA OF PASTIMES

Some Grown-ups exercise their bodies very slowly and calmly for hours.

Others use a bit more movement.

The AWFUL TRUTH about a lot of Grown-up
sports and pastimes is that they can be very
boring. For example. here is a Grown-up playing
a sport called Reading-the-Sunday-papers.

For a long time Grown-ups have been trying to get some of their sports included in the Olympic Games. Just imagine what that would mean . . .

Worse still, an AWFUL TRUTH is that Grown-ups are always trying to get you to take up one of their pastimes.

If you wake up one Saturday morning to find a bucket of soapy water and a sponge lying on your chest you'll know that a Grown-up wants you to try some car-washing.

Perhaps they will try to get you involved in the most dreaded pastime of all . . . **GARDENING.**

Firstly, they will make it sound so gentle
and nice . . .

But be prepared – it's a torture chamber
out there.

The Grown-up will say . . .

You're nice and strong – will you shift some stuff in the wheelbarrow for me?

Wheelbarrows have a mind of their own.

They will suddenly tip up just when you don't want them to.

Watch what you're doing!

You will get an Grown-up bark . . .

The Grown-up will say . . .

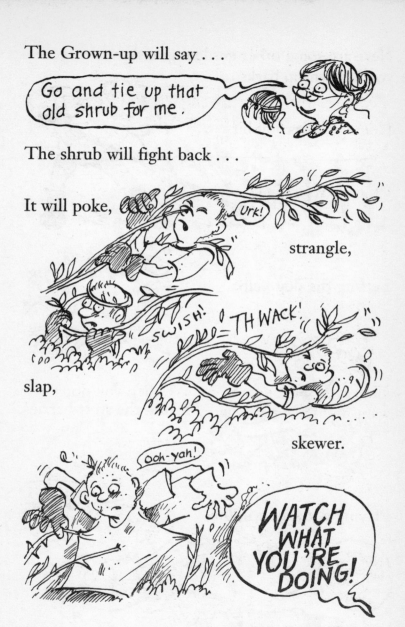

Go and tie up that old shrub for me.

The shrub will fight back . . .

It will poke,

Urk!

strangle,

SWISH!

THWACK!

slap,

skewer.

Ooh-yah!

WATCH WHAT YOU'RE DOING!

You will get another Grown-up bark . . .

Here are some other gardening tasks which get you Grown-up barks . . .

Hoeing the wrong bit.

Letting the dog help.

Picking the strawberries.

Playing with the wildlife.

Worst of all is poor handling of the garden hose, especially when other Grown-ups are around.

You will get a stupendous Grown-up bark.

STOP MUCKING ABOUT!

The AWFUL TRUTH is that Grown-ups take their sports and pastimes very seriously and you mustn't tease them about it.

THE AWFUL TRUTH ABOUT GROWN-UP EYESIGHT AND HEARING

Catamog has found out a few facts about Grown-up eyesight. The AWFUL TRUTH is that they are often as blind as bats.

Nice doggie!

PURRR

CATAMOG CATALOGUE PAGE 6
PIESTRIKE... EYESRIGHT... EYESIGHT...

For instance, many Grown-ups can't tell the difference between boys and girls.

Grown-up ears and noses aren't very good either.
Here is a view of a bit of the world through
Grown-up eyes, nose and ears.

UNTIDY HAIR THAT HASN'T SEEN A COMB IN WEEKS

BAGGY, BADLY-FITTING T-SHIRT THAT NEEDS A WASH

AWFUL, LOUD NOISE

DRAWERS THAT NEED A GOOD TIDY

THESE TROUSERS ARE A DISGRACE

HEAP OF JUNK

PONGY TRAINERS THAT OUGHT TO GO IN THE BIN

Here is the same view through the eyes, nose and ears of an ordinary, normal, not-grown-up human being.

RELAXED, NATURAL HAIRSTYLE

REALLY COMFY, LIVED-IN T-SHIRT

EXCELLENT MUSIC

EASY-TO-FIND FILING SYSTEM

FAVOURITE, SQUIDGY TROUSERS

COLLECTION OF INTERESTING THINGS

SWEET-SMELLING, FRIENDLY FOOTWEAR

Sometimes Grown-ups can be very deaf.

At other times their ears seem to be very sensitive.

The AWFUL TRUTH is that Grown-up eyes, ears and noses get worn out with overuse and they never think to have them serviced or renewed.

SOME COMMON PROBLEMS...

HAIR IN NOSTRILS AND EARS PREVENTS PROPER SMELLING AND HEARING.

Now where did I leave my glasses?

On the other hand, maybe it's best that way.

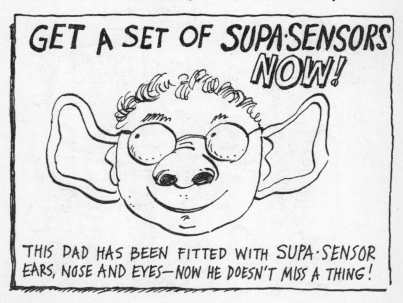

GET A SET OF SUPA·SENSORS NOW!

THIS DAD HAS BEEN FITTED WITH SUPA·SENSOR EARS, NOSE AND EYES—NOW HE DOESN'T MISS A THING!

THE AWFUL TRUTH ABOUT GROWN-UPS IN COATS

Some Grown-ups wear special coats. You have to be on your best behaviour when you're near a Grown-up in a coat. Catamog has been looking into coats.

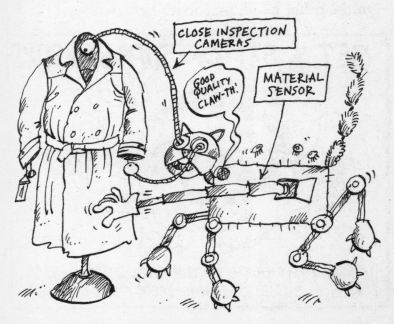

CLOSE INSPECTION CAMERAS

GOOD QUALITY CLAW-TH'

MATERIAL SENSOR

Look closely at the picture of the Lollipop Lady then look closely at the picture of the Samurai Warrior.

The AWFUL TRUTH is that there is no difference whatsoever.

The Lollipop Lady and the Samurai Warrior behave in much the same way. They are very courteous to the weak . . .

. . . and very dangerous to their enemies.

It's very rare to see two Lollipop Ladies together but if you do, it's best to be careful. They might fancy a game of Lollipop Lob.

Lollipop Lob is an unusual way of getting children across a busy road safely.

LOLLIPOP LADY AT OTHER SIDE OF ROAD CATCHES CHILD ON LOLLIPOP.

CHILD FLIPPED UPRIGHT ONTO PAVEMENT.

CATAMOG CATALOGUE PAGE B..

DIMPLE... DENT... DENTFIST... DENTIST...

When you go to the dentist you must sit in the waiting-room for hours. No one ever speaks and the magazines are incredibly boring.

The dentist always greets you with a cheery smile. This is so that you will smile back and he can get a good look at your teeth. It also gives him a chance to show off his teeth.

But the AWFUL TRUTH about dentists is that they have no manners at all. First of all, they ask you all sorts of questions but because they've filled up your mouth with bits of metal, you can't answer.

Then, because you won't answer, they ignore you and start talking to your teeth instead.

Dentists also encourage you to be bad-mannered by often telling you to spit.

One day, a door might swing open in your school and another Grown-up in a coat will enter. It's . . .
. . . the NIT NURSE!

BLAM!

If you've never had a nit nurse in school, then this is what happens . . .

EPISODE ONE

Your teacher will suddenly go silent when she spots something falling from someone's head.

A horrible expression will cross her face as she says in a quavery voice . . .

And everyone bends down to have a look which is just what the nits want.

The teacher dashes to the head teacher's office and says one word . . .

The head teacher immediately dials a special number.

In a far distant corner of the
country a phone rings . . .

. . . in Nit Nurse Castle.
It is answered by the Grand Nit Nurse.

72

A few minutes later a nurse speeds off on her special mission – to rid the children of these harmless little nits.

WHOOSH!

EPISODE THREE

The nit nurse arrives at school and orders the children to form a queue.

The AWFUL TRUTH is that the nit nurse will want to inspect every head in the school (maybe even the head's head) and spray nit-doom on it. Which means at least ten minutes off lessons.

The AWFUL TRUTH is that you have to treat Grown-ups in coats with special care. Here are a few more you might meet:

HEAD-THROUGH-THE-TOP COAT. OFTEN WORN BY SCHOOL DINNER LADIES. YOU SHOULD ALWAYS BE POLITE AND COMPLIMENTARY TO THEM (EVEN IF THE SHEPHERD'S PIE IS TRYING TO CLIMB OUT OF THE DISH) OTHERWISE THEY CAN TURN NASTY.

TRENDY BUSINESSMAN COAT. KEEP WELL CLEAR OF THESE FLAPPING COATS. THE OWNER WILL PROBABLY TRAMPLE YOU UNDERFOOT BECAUSE HE'S TOO BUSY TALKING ON HIS MOBILE PHONE.

SHOP ASSISTANT'S COAT. SHE'S PROBABLY YOUR BEST FRIEND'S BIG SISTER. SHE'LL PROBABLY TELL THE WHOLE NEIGHBOURHOOD WHAT YOU BOUGHT IN THE SHOP.

SCHOOL BUS-DRIVER'S COAT. ONLY TAKES IT OFF WHEN IT'S ABOVE 80°C. ALWAYS PRETEND TO LAUGH AT HIS AWFUL JOKES.

POLICEMAN'S BLACK MAC. ALWAYS WALK SLOWLY WHEN YOU SEE ONE OF THESE OR YOU'LL BE CHARGED WITH SPEEDING.

REALLY WEIRD COAT. IF YOU SEE SOMEONE WEARING A COAT LIKE THIS, THEN RUSH UP AND GET THEIR AUTOGRAPH BECAUSE THEY'RE PROBABLY SOMEONE FAMOUS.

75

THE AWFUL TRUTH ABOUT GROWN-UP HEADS

Catamog has decided to look at heads. He has noticed that Grown-ups are always tampering with their heads. They can't leave their heads at peace for a moment.

CATAMOG CATALOGUE PAGE 10

HI... HEDGEHOGS... HEAPS... HEADS...

CATAMOG HAS TAKEN HIS HEAD OFF SO HE CAN LOOK AT IT MORE CLOSELY.

Eh! where did it go?

Some Grown-ups see spots before their eyes. Or, at least, spots on their faces. They will fly into a panic if they think they have found a spot.

Always say 'Yes, I can see it – it's a great horrible thing.' This will make them very happy and they will go and stare at it in a mirror.

Grown-ups will spend hours every day lovingly looking after their spots.

Some Grown-ups like to hide their faces altogether. They usually do this by painting a new face on top of the old face.

Grown-ups have terrible trouble with their hair. If they go to get it cut they will give their hairdresser very careful instructions that take about half-an-hour.

After that they will check it every five minutes in the mirror.

Sometimes looking after hair becomes a really important event, like going to the cinema or a football match.

Grown-ups will spend all day in the hairdresser's drinking cups of coffee.

Grown-ups will also spend a lot of time looking for a hair that's not the same colour as the rest.

I'm sure I saw something grey yesterday!

Others will try to move parts of their hair to other bits of their head.

The AWFUL TRUTH is that Grown-ups are very sensitive about their heads . . .

. . . but have you ever seen a Grown-up with a normal head like yours?

THE AWFUL TRUTH ABOUT GROWN-UP TIME

Catamog has been checking up on Grown-ups' time-keeping. He's found some worrying facts about Grown-ups and clocks.

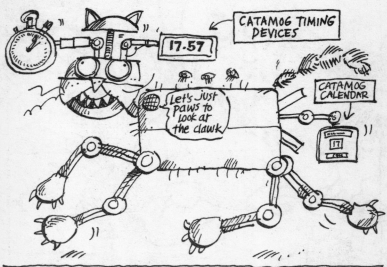

CATAMOG TIMING DEVICES

17·57

Let's just paws to look at the clawk

CATAMOG CALENDAR

17

CATAMOG CATALOGUE PAGE 11
TOTEM...TOM-TOM...TUMMY...TIME...

An **AWFUL TRUTH** about Grown-ups is that they have no sense of time whatsoever.

Sometimes they think there's no time left.

At other times, there's all the time in the world.
Grown-ups are always saying things like . . .

If you want to know what Grown-ups mean when they say these things, you need a special calculator.

Grown-ups will always have a meal ready when you don't want it.

And it won't be ready when you're starving.

They will always want to get you somewhere on time when you want to be late . . .

. . . and they'll get you somewhere late when you want to be on time.

Worst of all, just when the film on TV is reaching the most exciting bit they will say . . .

The AWFUL TRUTH is that you will just have to get used to the fact that Grown-ups live in a completely different time world from you.

THE AWFUL TRUTH ABOUT GROWN-UP EMBARRASSMENTS

Have you ever been embarrassed or annoyed? Catamog has found the AWFUL TRUTH that Grown-ups can make you feel like this sometimes. He has made a list of these embarrassments and annoyances.

RED WITH ANNOYANCE

EMBARRASSED AND ANNOYED FLEAS

RED WITH EMBARRASSMENT

CATAMOG CATALOGUE PAGE 12

ARMPITS... UMBRELLAS... EMBERS... EMBA...

Grown-ups who think they're babies.

Grown-ups who think
they're animals.

Grown-ups who drag you along by the arm in a busy street.

Grown-ups who won't let you near the computer, especially when they're playing one of your games.

Grown-ups who tell stories about themselves in front of your friends.

Grown-ups who tell stories about *you* in front of your friends.

Grown-ups who shout loudly across a busy shop.

Grown-ups who buy you the wrong, soppy, drink.

Grown-ups who sing loudly in the car.

Grown-ups who wear silly clothes to the
Christmas Concert.

Grown-ups who give you a big, wet, long, noisy
kiss in public.

Catamog has finished his catalogue about Grown-ups.
Here are his final words:

The AWFUL TRUTH is that *you* will be a
Grown-up one day, so BE WARNED.

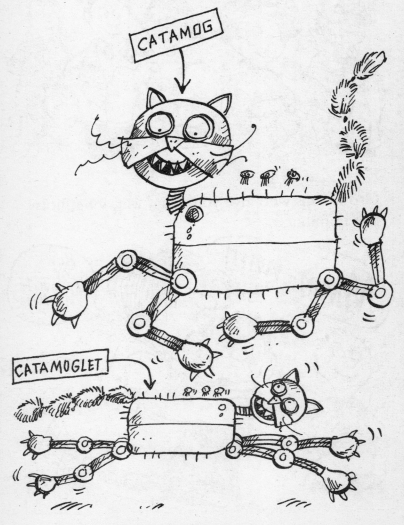

CATAMOG

CATAMOGLET